This logbook contains vital information about my recreational vehicle (RV).

If found, please return to:

Name _____

Address _____

City _____

State _____   **Zip** _____

Cell Phone Number _____

Home Phone Number _____

e-Mail Address _____

Thank you.

Caution: **Only reveal the contact information you believe is necessary.**

My RV
"LOGBOOK"

An Vital Record of My RV's Equipment & Appliance Information

Part of the "Understanding Your RV" Series of Books

Other Published RV books
*available at **www.sumdalus.com***

Understanding Your RV's "SHOREPOWER"
120 Volt Electricity

Understanding Your RV's "APPLIANCES"
Refrigerator, Furnace, Water Heater, and Rooftop Air Conditioner

Understanding Your RV's "HOLDING TANKS"
Bio-Waste Management
(or **What You Don't Know About Your Holding Tanks**)

Understanding Your RV's "BATTERY POWER"
12 Volt Electricity

Published by SUMDALUS-USA
P.O. Box 186
Zephyrhills, FL 33539

Printed in the United States of America.
ISBN-13: 978-0-9974634-4-6

<u>DEDICATED TO</u>

Ms. Kellye Janis, a driving force behind RVPartfinder.com, a multifaceted RV parts information repository. This website application is, without a doubt, the RV industry's crème de la crème parts research tool.

Kellye's enthusiasm for the RV industry has always been exceptionally passionate. Her sincere work ethic and her honest concern for the success of all her "customers" are unwavering.

Thank you, Kellye, for all your support and encouragement.

Keep up the GREAT work!

DISCLAIMER

If you are the do-it-yourself (DIY) repair type, please be aware, you are responsible for any hazards you encounter or produce if you "work" on or attempt to "fix" anything in or on your RV. Your legal right to work on some parts of your RV may be limited in your State. Contacting a local RV dealership to schedule a "bring it in" appointment, or contacting a local, independent RV service technician to "come to" your RV site are always options and may be required to accomplish necessary adjustments or repairs.

NOTE

Most photographs, images, diagrams, or charts not sourced/credited within this book were designed and/or produced by the author. The publisher has made reasonable effort to contact all identifiable copyright holders. Any errors that may have occurred are inadvertent and anyone who, for any reason, has not been contacted is invited to write to the publisher so that a full acknowledgment may be made in subsequent editions of this work.

INTRODUCTION

A logbook ('la:g͵bʊk) is defined by Webster's dictionary as "a written record of information, activity, or events."

This "logbook" was specifically written to assist the typical RVer (**J.** {Jane or John} **Q. Public**) with the collection of critical data about their RV. As a self-recorded compendium of all the equipment and appliance's Manufacturer's Product Label Data, this concisely laid-out logbook will assist any repair facility to quickly identify and find the correct part(s) needed to accomplish a requested repair. Furthermore, documenting all your service/repair history in this logbook may enhance the resale value of your RV!

Located on Page 30, is a suggested list of Equipment and Appliance items which should be considered for data recording. Choose those items most applicable to your RV.

The layouts of the data entry sections are based upon the author's personal RV information and maintenance records. Admittedly, something elemental may have been accidently overlooked. If you have any improvement ideas for future editions, please feel free to submit your recommendations via the "Contact Us" link at **www.sumdalus.com**. Thank you.

What an RV is <u>NOT</u>. . .

As a matter of practice, I always start every one of my RVing seminars with this simple, but often unrealized fact, *"Ladies and Gentlemen, a Recreational Vehicle (RV) is <u>NOT</u> a House and should not be treated or ignored as though it was!"*

Although many RV owners want to use their motorhome, travel trailer, or 5th wheel trailer as though it was a house, it certainly is not! The interior of an RV may look and feel like a house, but, foremost, the RV can move from place to place while a house cannot. This movement capability has its own significant set of issues.

The RV specific appliances (refrigerator, furnace, water heater, and air conditioner) resemble house appliances, but they are not built the same, nor do they really function the same. It's important to know just "how" they do work.

The RV's 120 Volt electrical capability is very different than a typical three-bedroom house – a 50 Amp RV is 50% <u>less</u> capable and a 30 Amp RV is 85% <u>less</u> capable. This reduced capability demands a need for understanding the inherent limitations, as well as the need for "whole RV electrical protection."

The RV's 12 Volt "house" battery system is nothing like a typical car battery system. As the largest single system in any RV, it certainly requires a great deal more attention and maintenance.

And, the RV's bio-waste system is nothing like a typical domestic septic tank system, but is rather a "temporary" holding system. If you avoid dealing with this system properly, it's likely to become "unhealthy." And, if does, it's more than likely <u>you</u> won't be healthy for long.

Furthermore, let's not overlook the simple fact that <u>not</u> one single RV manufacturer has ever designed and/or con- structed any RV to be lived in, permanently, like a house.

And finally, every RV built requires a great deal more maintenance than <u>any</u> house on the market! Yep, that's right, there is no such thing as a maintenance-free RV. That's because RVs aren't designed or built to be a "durable good," as evidenced by the fact that all RVs have a warranty period that is much shorter than the least expensive, new car on today's market.

So..., now that you have an inkling that the two "living spaces" are dissimilar and there may be some unaccustomed responsibilities that you will be required to accomplish when dealing with an RV, this logbook will permit you to record some of your RV's distinctive attributes.

With all that said, let's cover a few things you may not have known about an RV . . .

The following brief topics expand on the practical application of "an RV is NOT a House."

Expectations

While all RV manufacturers produce recreational vehicles (RVs) to different proprietary specifications, we expect each new RV to be equipped with up-to-date, state-of-the-art systems, appliances, and over-the-road operational equipment. And, like any other complex assembly of equipment and parts, we should also expect that each RV will require a substantial amount of tender-loving-care and regular maintenance to preserve its interior and exterior appearance, as well as ensure its consistent optimal performance (not to mention its resale value).

Owner's Manuals

The RV's User/Owner Manuals (or, if there isn't one, at least the manufacturer's user/owner's manuals for the individual equipments/appliances) are written to aid us in understanding the proper use, operation, and maintenance of the diverse components and systems assembled within our RV. Considering the latter expectation, above, it behooves every one of us to carefully read and annotate/hilite important information within each applicable user/owner's manual we can get our hands on.

(**Comment:** And, yes, we all quickly become fully aware of the limitations of many of the available manuals. That's what prompted me to start writing the "Understanding Your RV" series of books in the first place)

Construction Codes

Another expectation we all have is that the RV we are about to purchase (or already own) has been constructed in compliance with all codes and standards applicable to the RV industry. Fortunately, there is a governing body which oversees this situation. It is the Standards Department of the Recreation Vehicle Industry Association (RVIA). It serves as the administrator of the RVIA Inspection Program based on adopted standards for construction of recreational vehicles (there are more than 500 standards for every RV and Park Model). They periodically inspect to ensure that strict adherence to their safety standards is maintained. Certification can be verified by their Seal, which is distinctively affixed to the body of the RV, near the opening side of the entrance door. (Now, you know what that oval-shaped seal is all about!)

<u>Seal Color Coding</u>

Gold and Black – Motorhomes.

Silver and Black – 5th Wheel and
other Travel Trailers.

White and Black – Truck Campers and
Folding Camping Trailers.

[Source: RVIA.org]

Basic RV Warranty Information

THE WHOLE RV: While very specific in nature, most RV manufacturers have just a <u>one-year</u> warranty covering what they produce. This warranty typically states that the RV manufacturer will fix any defective items or possible mistakes made during manufacturing.

(**Comment:** Some manufacturers have distinctive warranty periods for different components of the RV. [e.g. Motorhomes usually have at least two warranties – one for the coach (living area) and one for the chassis/powertrain (undercarriage) components.])

If you are in "research" mode before making an initial (or subsequent) purchase of a new RV, ask the sales-person/dealer to see a copy of the manufacturer's actual warranty information for any model you are seriously considering purchasing. Make sure you read it carefully before signing on the dotted line.)

APPLIANCES: On the other warranty hand, most of the appliance manufacturers have two-year warranties on their products. However, with any recreational vehicle "unique" appliance, there is an absolute need for routine care and appropriate maintenance.

(*Comment:* I have found, over the years, that most warranty work requests are due to the owner's misunderstanding of some of the operating features of the RV's unique components, rather than actual equipment failure.)

Routine Care always helps prevent the unfortunate consequence of sidelining your RV for Warranty Work. Appropriate Maintenance (and timely, i.e. typically, *annual service)*, is mandated, in writing, by all RV refrigerator, furnace, water heater, and air conditioner manufacturers. Failure to provide proof of compliance may result in denial of warranty coverage.

(*Comment:* I strongly recommend you read each appliance's User/Owner's Manual very carefully – especially the warranty requirements. Check online if you weren't provided the applicable manuals.)

Caution: When taking possession of a new RV, make sure the dealer provides you with all the applicable individual product warranty registrations. (e.g. refrigerator, water heater, furnace, TV, microwave, range/cooktop, etc.) Be sure you fill these cards out completely and mail them promptly.

Note: During your first year of ownership, your RV appliances are essentially covered by two warranties – under the RV manufacturer's warranty and, also, under the appliance manufacturer's warranty. The RV appliances are specific Brand Names (i.e. not made by the RV manufacturer) and, therefore, an appliance manufacturer may provide you more expedient repair if that manufacturer has an authorized repair facility or service center relatively close to you – especially important if the appliance is a "standard" house appliance and not an RV "unique" appliance.

Extended Warranty

This type of warranty is also known as a Service Contract or Extended Service Contract. They are sold separately by the dealership or by an independent broker. It usually covers specific components of the RV after the manufacturer's warranty expires.

(**Comment:** I am especially wary of extended warranty plans that overlap the RV manufacturer's original warranty. Why pay for coverage that's already there?)

Check out what's being offered very closely. What you're ideally looking for is called an <u>Exclusionary Contract</u>. This one tends to cover most mechanical aspects of your RV **except** for what is specifically "Excluded from Coverage," listed as "Exclusions," or "What is Not Covered" in the contract. And, don't forget to become specifically familiar with any "<u>pre-repair authorization</u>" requirements (i.e. authorization must be received BEFORE any repairs are started)!

By all means, no matter which type of Extended Warranty you are looking at, please read all of the fine print carefully – something in there could be a deal breaker.

Unwritten Owner Responsibility

As an unwritten, but fair and reasonable, principle, it has always been acknowledged that, during any RV manufacturer's stated Warranty Period (as well as afterward), the responsibility rests with the owners to properly maintain their RVs. Besides performing routine, manufacturer recommended, and scheduled maintenance, this especially includes taking all preventative actions and/or contractual arrangements necessary to regularly inspect and maintain all the exterior sealants on the RV – the lack of sealant maintenance is the major cause of ensuing interior, flooring, or even structural damage.

Make the commitment –

I will always be a responsible RV owner, and will, thereby, protect my investment.

What you need to know when calling about a Service/Repair Need

Let's say the air conditioner in your RV is not cooling like it should. Naturally, you call a service facility (i.e. RV dealership or mobile repair) to see if they can fix it. When the service representative asks you, "which model do you have," you proudly respond that you have "a 'such and such' model of a 'two thousand and something' Super Brand RV." You even have the vehicle identification number (VIN) ready to recite, just in case. However, what the service representative <u>really</u> meant…was, "which model <u>air</u> <u>conditioner</u> do you have?" – because <u>that's</u> what you had asked about having fixed.

Oops! You just learned a major difference between the RV industry and the automotive industry. Contrary to common expectations, unless you are requesting work to be done on the chassis (or powertrain), supplying the Year, Make, and Model, or the VIN of <u>your RV</u> to a repair facility, will **<u>NOT</u>** provide the service personnel with an exact listing of which equipment/ appliances exist on, in, or under your RV (e.g. air conditioner/heat pump, awning, furnace, refrigerator, television and/or antenna, toilet, water heater, etc., etc.).

Unfortunately, the RV industry does not "link" any of the diverse equipment/appliance information to each uniquely assembled RV model or VIN. The exact items any RV manufacturer may have installed during the "initial build" is a mystery and requires someone to make the effort to examine your "distinctively built" RV for specific data - every time a service/repair is requested.

(**Remember:** Except for specific fabrication design(s), the RV manufacturers are basically assemblers of various, independently manufactured components that make up their distinct RV models.)

Because of this regrettable lack of information consolidation, it behooves each RV owner to accumulate and maintain this important information for themselves.

A partial example of such an information list is demonstrated below:

Equip/Appl Name:	Toilet	Water Heater	Refrigerator	Furnace
Manufacturer:	Dometic	Dometic	Dometic	Dometic
Brand Name:	Sealand	Atwood	Americana	Atwood
Model:	Traveler	Exothermal (XT)	RM2663	Excalibur
Serial Number:	12345	67890	54321	09876
Product Number:	2010	GE16EXT	921144136	8535-IV
Color/Finish:	Bone	Polar White	Black Inserts	Polar White
Size/Rating:	17.5"	16 Gal	6 cu. ft.	34K BTU

p.s. This information is normally found on the manufacturer's product data label located on each equipment/ appliance. (**Note:** Label locations vary.)

(*Comment:* Yes, this level of <u>specific</u> <u>detail</u> is, indeed, necessary for the service technician or parts-counter worker to be able to correctly identify and locate any required repair parts for your improperly functioning equipment/appliance. So…, be very thorough when collecting data. If you have all this information readily available, in advance, you will help expedite the time necessary to accomplish your requested service/repair need. As a friend of mine in the RV Repair Parts business has often advocated, "If you want the right part(s) the <u>first</u> time, simply provide the proper information to make it happen." Hmmm – sounds like good advice.)

(*Additional Comment:* Documenting all your service/repair history in this concisely laid-out logbook may enhance the resale value of your RV – it certainly has for me, repeatedly.)

Here's **another "Oops"** you need to be aware of. When a service representative asks you "what <u>type</u> of RV do you have?" s/he is **not** asking you about the Year, Make, <u>or</u> Model of your RV. The question refers to the specific category (a.k.a. "Class") of RV you have. There are seven (7) uniquely different "<u>types</u>" of RVs:

Class A

(Author's Coach)

Class B

Class C

Travel Trailer

5th Wheel

Truck Camper

Folding Tent Camper

Notes:

Now that you have some fundamental ideas about, expectations, manuals, codes, warranties, as well as **"how"** to answer the basic service questions, let's start collecting some important data that you, more than likely, <u>will</u> need to provide to an RV service representative/technician.

This logbook is laid out in four sections:

1. **Dealer/Seller and RV Information & Service Records**

   Pages specifically oriented to the "whole" RV.

2. **Equipment/Appliance Information & Service Records**

   One page for each named Equip/Appl. If you have two of the same Equip/Appl (e.g. Air Conditioner and/or Furnace) identify one as Front or Rear (or Left or Right) and the other as the opposite. There are ample blank rows on each Equip/ Appl page where you may add optional information you discover and want to incorporate into the logbook.

3. **Continuation of Service/Repair Record Information**

   These pages are provided for use "as necessary." You can link your Service/Repair Record information pages together by using the "Continued on Page #" annotation field at the bottom of the applicable Service/Repair Record page, as well as back-referencing the "Name" and "Page #" annotation fields at the top of the appropriate Continuation Page.

4. **Index**

   This Index is distinctly different. The basic Topics are already incorporated. However, the users are requested to identify the Name of the self-entered Equipment or Appliance Items and their Page Numbers The same is true for the Continuation Pages.

Dealership/Seller and RV Information

&

Service Records

The following pages are specifically oriented to information pertaining to the "whole" RV.

- Dealership/Seller
- Important Phone Numbers
- Multifarious Information
- Service/Repair Information

Information pertaining to the "whole" RV

Purchase Date:	
From:	
Location:	
Phone Number:	
Website:	
Salesperson:	
Phone Number:	
Extension:	
e-Mail Address:	
Year:	
Manufacturer:	
Brand Name:	
Model:	
Length (Ft. In.)	
Serial Number:	
VIN Number:	
Color(s):	

Notes:

Other Important Information pertaining to the "whole" RV

Notes:

Important RV Dealership Phone Numbers

Customer Service	
Events	
Finance	
Parts Department	
Rentals	
Resort/Campground	
Sales	
Service/Repair	
Store	
Tech Support	

Other Important Phone Numbers

Important Multifarious Information

Weights:	
Empty (Dry) Weight	
Hitch (Tongue) Weight	
GVWR	
Allowable Load Weight	
GCWR	
Allowable Towing Wt.	
Capacities:	
Fresh Water Tank	
Gray Water Tank	
Black Water Tank	
LP Cylinder(s)/Tank	
Fuel Tank	
House Battery(s):	
Voltage (6 or 12 VDC)	
Group	
Type (Lead Acid or AGM)	
Manufacturer/Brand	
Model/Part Number	
Quantity	
Engine Battery(s):	
Voltage	
Group	
Type (Lead Acid or AGM)	
Manufacturer/Brand	
Model/Part Number	
Quantity	

Other Important Multifarious Information

Tires:	
Manufacturer	
Model	
Tire Size	
Maximum Tire Pressure (Cold)	
Mfr Date & Tire Position	(e.g. 5017 – Rt Frt)
Tire Pressure & Axle Position	(e.g. 95 psi – Frt)

Other Important Multifarious Information

Other Important Multifarious Information

Service/Repair Data for "Whole" RV

Service/Repair Date:	
Performed by:	
Service/Repair Accomplished:	

Service/Repair Date:	
Performed by:	
Service/Repair Accomplished:	

Service/Repair Date:	
Performed by:	
Service/Repair Accomplished:	

Service/Repair Date:	
Performed by:	
Service/Repair Accomplished:	

Service/Repair Date:	
Performed by:	
Service/Repair Accomplished:	

Service/Repair Data for "Whole" RV

Service/Repair Date:	
Performed by:	
Service/Repair Accomplished:	

Service/Repair Date:	
Performed by:	
Service/Repair Accomplished:	

Service/Repair Date:	
Performed by:	
Service/Repair Accomplished:	

Service/Repair Date:	
Performed by:	
Service/Repair Accomplished:	

Service/Repair Date:	
Performed by:	
Service/Repair Accomplished:	

Continued on Page # _____

A Suggested List of Equipments/Appliances.
Choose the items applicable to your RV:

AC/DC Power Center (MCBP)
Air Conditioner(s)/Heat Pump(s)
Automatic Load Shed System
Automatic Transfer Switch
Converter
Cooktop
Dishwasher
Door Awning
Electrical Protection System
Exhaust Fans
Fire Extinguisher
Furnace
Generator
Inverter
LP Regulator
Microwave
Patio Awning
Range
Rear View Camera System
Refrigerator
Satellite Antenna
Toilet
TV Antenna
Vacuum System
Washer/Dryer
Water Heater
Water Pump
Window Awnings

(There may be more...)

Equipment/Appliance Information

&

Service Records

Hint: While simply removing an access panel or cover is the norm, if you are unable to locate the Manufacturer's Product Data Label without significantly dismantling the equipment/appliance, ask the service representative/technician to transcribe the information for you while that particular item is being serviced/repaired for the first time. (A team effort works best.)

Information Pertaining to Named Equipment or Appliance

Equip/Appl Name:	
Manufacturer:	
Brand Name:	
Model:	
Serial Number:	
Product Number:	
Color/Finish:	
Size/Rating:	
Misc:	
Purchase Date:	
From:	
Installation Date:	
Performed by:	
Notes:	

Service/Repair Date:	
Performed by:	

Service/Repair Accomplished:

Service/Repair Date:	
Performed by:	

Service/Repair Accomplished:

Service/Repair Date:	
Performed by:	

Service/Repair Accomplished:

Service/Repair Date:	
Performed by:	

Service/Repair Accomplished:

Service/Repair Date:	
Performed by:	

Service/Repair Accomplished:

Service/Repair Date:	
Performed by:	

Service/Repair Accomplished:

Continued on Page # _____

Information Pertaining to Named Equipment or Appliance

Equip/Appl Name:	
Manufacturer:	
Brand Name:	
Model:	
Serial Number:	
Product Number:	
Color/Finish:	
Size/Rating:	
Misc:	
Purchase Date:	
From:	
Installation Date:	
Performed by:	
Notes:	

Service/Repair Date:	
Performed by:	

Service/Repair Accomplished:

Service/Repair Date:	
Performed by:	

Service/Repair Accomplished:

Service/Repair Date:	
Performed by:	

Service/Repair Accomplished:

Service/Repair Date:	
Performed by:	

Service/Repair Accomplished:

Service/Repair Date:	
Performed by:	

Service/Repair Accomplished:

Service/Repair Date:	
Performed by:	

Service/Repair Accomplished:

Continued on Page # _____

Information Pertaining to Named Equipment or Appliance

Equip/Appl Name:	
Manufacturer:	
Brand Name:	
Model:	
Serial Number:	
Product Number:	
Color/Finish:	
Size/Rating:	
Misc:	
Purchase Date:	
From:	
Installation Date:	
Performed by:	
Notes:	

Service/Repair Date:	
Performed by:	

Service/Repair Accomplished:

Service/Repair Date:	
Performed by:	

Service/Repair Accomplished:

Service/Repair Date:	
Performed by:	

Service/Repair Accomplished:

Service/Repair Date:	
Performed by:	

Service/Repair Accomplished:

Service/Repair Date:	
Performed by:	

Service/Repair Accomplished:

Service/Repair Date:	
Performed by:	

Service/Repair Accomplished:

Continued on Page # _____

Information Pertaining to Named Equipment or Appliance

Equip/Appl Name:	
Manufacturer:	
Brand Name:	
Model:	
Serial Number:	
Product Number:	
Color/Finish:	
Size/Rating:	
Misc:	
Purchase Date:	
From:	
Installation Date:	
Performed by:	
Notes:	

Service/Repair Date:	
Performed by:	

Service/Repair Accomplished:

Service/Repair Date:	
Performed by:	

Service/Repair Accomplished:

Service/Repair Date:	
Performed by:	

Service/Repair Accomplished:

Service/Repair Date:	
Performed by:	

Service/Repair Accomplished:

Service/Repair Date:	
Performed by:	

Service/Repair Accomplished:

Service/Repair Date:	
Performed by:	

Service/Repair Accomplished:

Continued on Page # _____

Information Pertaining to Named Equipment or Appliance

Equip/Appl Name:	
Manufacturer:	
Brand Name:	
Model:	
Serial Number:	
Product Number:	
Color/Finish:	
Size/Rating:	
Misc:	
Purchase Date:	
From:	
Installation Date:	
Performed by:	
Notes:	

Service/Repair Date:	
Performed by:	
Service/Repair Accomplished:	

Service/Repair Date:	
Performed by:	
Service/Repair Accomplished:	

Service/Repair Date:	
Performed by:	
Service/Repair Accomplished:	

Service/Repair Date:	
Performed by:	
Service/Repair Accomplished:	

Service/Repair Date:	
Performed by:	
Service/Repair Accomplished:	

Service/Repair Date:	
Performed by:	
Service/Repair Accomplished:	

Continued on Page # _____

Information Pertaining to Named Equipment or Appliance

Equip/Appl Name:	
Manufacturer:	
Brand Name:	
Model:	
Serial Number:	
Product Number:	
Color/Finish:	
Size/Rating:	
Misc:	
Purchase Date:	
From:	
Installation Date:	
Performed by:	
Notes:	

Service/Repair Date:	
Performed by:	
Service/Repair Accomplished:	

Service/Repair Date:	
Performed by:	
Service/Repair Accomplished:	

Service/Repair Date:	
Performed by:	
Service/Repair Accomplished:	

Service/Repair Date:	
Performed by:	
Service/Repair Accomplished:	

Service/Repair Date:	
Performed by:	
Service/Repair Accomplished:	

Service/Repair Date:	
Performed by:	
Service/Repair Accomplished:	

Continued on Page # _____

Information Pertaining to Named Equipment or Appliance

Equip/Appl Name:	
Manufacturer:	
Brand Name:	
Model:	
Serial Number:	
Product Number:	
Color/Finish:	
Size/Rating:	
Misc:	
Purchase Date:	
From:	
Installation Date:	
Performed by:	
Notes:	

Service/Repair Date:	
Performed by:	

Service/Repair Accomplished:

Service/Repair Date:	
Performed by:	

Service/Repair Accomplished:

Service/Repair Date:	
Performed by:	

Service/Repair Accomplished:

Service/Repair Date:	
Performed by:	

Service/Repair Accomplished:

Service/Repair Date:	
Performed by:	

Service/Repair Accomplished:

Service/Repair Date:	
Performed by:	

Service/Repair Accomplished:

Continued on Page # _____

Information Pertaining to Named Equipment or Appliance

Equip/Appl Name:	
Manufacturer:	
Brand Name:	
Model:	
Serial Number:	
Product Number:	
Color/Finish:	
Size/Rating:	
Misc:	
Purchase Date:	
From:	
Installation Date:	
Performed by:	
Notes:	

Service/Repair Date:	
Performed by:	
Service/Repair Accomplished:	

Service/Repair Date:	
Performed by:	
Service/Repair Accomplished:	

Service/Repair Date:	
Performed by:	
Service/Repair Accomplished:	

Service/Repair Date:	
Performed by:	
Service/Repair Accomplished:	

Service/Repair Date:	
Performed by:	
Service/Repair Accomplished:	

Service/Repair Date:	
Performed by:	
Service/Repair Accomplished:	

Continued on Page # _____

Information Pertaining to Named
Equipment or Appliance

Equip/Appl Name:	
Manufacturer:	
Brand Name:	
Model:	
Serial Number:	
Product Number:	
Color/Finish:	
Size/Rating:	
Misc:	
Purchase Date:	
From:	
Installation Date:	
Performed by:	
Notes:	

Service/Repair Date:	
Performed by:	

Service/Repair Accomplished:

Service/Repair Date:	
Performed by:	

Service/Repair Accomplished:

Service/Repair Date:	
Performed by:	

Service/Repair Accomplished:

Service/Repair Date:	
Performed by:	

Service/Repair Accomplished:

Service/Repair Date:	
Performed by:	

Service/Repair Accomplished:

Service/Repair Date:	
Performed by:	

Service/Repair Accomplished:

Continued on Page # _____

Information Pertaining to Named Equipment or Appliance

Equip/Appl Name:	
Manufacturer:	
Brand Name:	
Model:	
Serial Number:	
Product Number:	
Color/Finish:	
Size/Rating:	
Misc:	
Purchase Date:	
From:	
Installation Date:	
Performed by:	
Notes:	

Service/Repair Date:	
Performed by:	
Service/Repair Accomplished:	

Service/Repair Date:	
Performed by:	
Service/Repair Accomplished:	

Service/Repair Date:	
Performed by:	
Service/Repair Accomplished:	

Service/Repair Date:	
Performed by:	
Service/Repair Accomplished:	

Service/Repair Date:	
Performed by:	
Service/Repair Accomplished:	

Service/Repair Date:	
Performed by:	
Service/Repair Accomplished:	

Continued on Page # _____

Information Pertaining to Named
Equipment or Appliance

Equip/Appl Name:	
Manufacturer:	
Brand Name:	
Model:	
Serial Number:	
Product Number:	
Color/Finish:	
Size/Rating:	
Misc:	
Purchase Date:	
From:	
Installation Date:	
Performed by:	
Notes:	

Service/Repair Date:	
Performed by:	
Service/Repair Accomplished:	

Service/Repair Date:	
Performed by:	
Service/Repair Accomplished:	

Service/Repair Date:	
Performed by:	
Service/Repair Accomplished:	

Service/Repair Date:	
Performed by:	
Service/Repair Accomplished:	

Service/Repair Date:	
Performed by:	
Service/Repair Accomplished:	

Service/Repair Date:	
Performed by:	
Service/Repair Accomplished:	

Continued on Page # _____

Information Pertaining to Named Equipment or Appliance

Equip/Appl Name:	
Manufacturer:	
Brand Name:	
Model:	
Serial Number:	
Product Number:	
Color/Finish:	
Size/Rating:	
Misc:	
Purchase Date:	
From:	
Installation Date:	
Performed by:	
Notes:	

Service/Repair Date:	
Performed by:	
Service/Repair Accomplished:	

Service/Repair Date:	
Performed by:	
Service/Repair Accomplished:	

Service/Repair Date:	
Performed by:	
Service/Repair Accomplished:	

Service/Repair Date:	
Performed by:	
Service/Repair Accomplished:	

Service/Repair Date:	
Performed by:	
Service/Repair Accomplished:	

Service/Repair Date:	
Performed by:	
Service/Repair Accomplished:	

Continued on Page # _____

Information Pertaining to Named
Equipment or Appliance

Equip/Appl Name:	
Manufacturer:	
Brand Name:	
Model:	
Serial Number:	
Product Number:	
Color/Finish:	
Size/Rating:	
Misc:	
Purchase Date:	
From:	
Installation Date:	
Performed by:	
Notes:	

Service/Repair Date:	
Performed by:	
Service/Repair Accomplished:	

Service/Repair Date:	
Performed by:	
Service/Repair Accomplished:	

Service/Repair Date:	
Performed by:	
Service/Repair Accomplished:	

Service/Repair Date:	
Performed by:	
Service/Repair Accomplished:	

Service/Repair Date:	
Performed by:	
Service/Repair Accomplished:	

Service/Repair Date:	
Performed by:	
Service/Repair Accomplished:	

Continued on Page # _____

Information Pertaining to Named Equipment or Appliance

Equip/Appl Name:	
Manufacturer:	
Brand Name:	
Model:	
Serial Number:	
Product Number:	
Color/Finish:	
Size/Rating:	
Misc:	
Purchase Date:	
From:	
Installation Date:	
Performed by:	
Notes:	

Service/Repair Date:	
Performed by:	

Service/Repair Accomplished:

Service/Repair Date:	
Performed by:	

Service/Repair Accomplished:

Service/Repair Date:	
Performed by:	

Service/Repair Accomplished:

Service/Repair Date:	
Performed by:	

Service/Repair Accomplished:

Service/Repair Date:	
Performed by:	

Service/Repair Accomplished:

Service/Repair Date:	
Performed by:	

Service/Repair Accomplished:

Continued on Page # _____

Information Pertaining to Named Equipment or Appliance

Equip/Appl Name:	
Manufacturer:	
Brand Name:	
Model:	
Serial Number:	
Product Number:	
Color/Finish:	
Size/Rating:	
Misc:	
Purchase Date:	
From:	
Installation Date:	
Performed by:	
Notes:	

Service/Repair Date:	
Performed by:	
Service/Repair Accomplished:	

Service/Repair Date:	
Performed by:	
Service/Repair Accomplished:	

Service/Repair Date:	
Performed by:	
Service/Repair Accomplished:	

Service/Repair Date:	
Performed by:	
Service/Repair Accomplished:	

Service/Repair Date:	
Performed by:	
Service/Repair Accomplished:	

Service/Repair Date:	
Performed by:	
Service/Repair Accomplished:	

Continued on Page # _____

Information Pertaining to Named Equipment or Appliance

Equip/Appl Name:	
Manufacturer:	
Brand Name:	
Model:	
Serial Number:	
Product Number:	
Color/Finish:	
Size/Rating:	
Misc:	
Purchase Date:	
From:	
Installation Date:	
Performed by:	
Notes:	

Service/Repair Date:	
Performed by:	

Service/Repair Accomplished:

Service/Repair Date:	
Performed by:	

Service/Repair Accomplished:

Service/Repair Date:	
Performed by:	

Service/Repair Accomplished:

Service/Repair Date:	
Performed by:	

Service/Repair Accomplished:

Service/Repair Date:	
Performed by:	

Service/Repair Accomplished:

Service/Repair Date:	
Performed by:	

Service/Repair Accomplished:

Continued on Page # _____

Information Pertaining to Named Equipment or Appliance

Equip/Appl Name:	
Manufacturer:	
Brand Name:	
Model:	
Serial Number:	
Product Number:	
Color/Finish:	
Size/Rating:	
Misc:	
Purchase Date:	
From:	
Installation Date:	
Performed by:	
Notes:	

Service/Repair Date:	
Performed by:	

Service/Repair Accomplished:

Service/Repair Date:	
Performed by:	

Service/Repair Accomplished:

Service/Repair Date:	
Performed by:	

Service/Repair Accomplished:

Service/Repair Date:	
Performed by:	

Service/Repair Accomplished:

Service/Repair Date:	
Performed by:	

Service/Repair Accomplished:

Service/Repair Date:	
Performed by:	

Service/Repair Accomplished:

Continued on Page # _____

Information Pertaining to Named Equipment or Appliance

Equip/Appl Name:	
Manufacturer:	
Brand Name:	
Model:	
Serial Number:	
Product Number:	
Color/Finish:	
Size/Rating:	
Misc:	
Purchase Date:	
From:	
Installation Date:	
Performed by:	
Notes:	

Service/Repair Date:	
Performed by:	
Service/Repair Accomplished:	

Service/Repair Date:	
Performed by:	
Service/Repair Accomplished:	

Service/Repair Date:	
Performed by:	
Service/Repair Accomplished:	

Service/Repair Date:	
Performed by:	
Service/Repair Accomplished:	

Service/Repair Date:	
Performed by:	
Service/Repair Accomplished:	

Service/Repair Date:	
Performed by:	
Service/Repair Accomplished:	

Continued on Page # _____

Information Pertaining to Named Equipment or Appliance

Equip/Appl Name:	
Manufacturer:	
Brand Name:	
Model:	
Serial Number:	
Product Number:	
Color/Finish:	
Size/Rating:	
Misc:	
Purchase Date:	
From:	
Installation Date:	
Performed by:	
Notes:	

Service/Repair Date:	
Performed by:	

Service/Repair Accomplished:

Service/Repair Date:	
Performed by:	

Service/Repair Accomplished:

Service/Repair Date:	
Performed by:	

Service/Repair Accomplished:

Service/Repair Date:	
Performed by:	

Service/Repair Accomplished:

Service/Repair Date:	
Performed by:	

Service/Repair Accomplished:

Service/Repair Date:	
Performed by:	

Service/Repair Accomplished:

Continued on Page # _____

Information Pertaining to Named Equipment or Appliance

Equip/Appl Name:	
Manufacturer:	
Brand Name:	
Model:	
Serial Number:	
Product Number:	
Color/Finish:	
Size/Rating:	
Misc:	
Purchase Date:	
From:	
Installation Date:	
Performed by:	
Notes:	

Service/Repair Date:	
Performed by:	
Service/Repair Accomplished:	

Service/Repair Date:	
Performed by:	
Service/Repair Accomplished:	

Service/Repair Date:	
Performed by:	
Service/Repair Accomplished:	

Service/Repair Date:	
Performed by:	
Service/Repair Accomplished:	

Service/Repair Date:	
Performed by:	
Service/Repair Accomplished:	

Service/Repair Date:	
Performed by:	
Service/Repair Accomplished:	

Continued on Page # _____

Notes

Continuation of Service/
Repair Record Information

These pages are provided for use "as necessary." You should link your Service/Repair Record information pages together by using the "Continued on Page #" annotation field at the bottom of the applicable Service/Repair Record page, as well as back-referencing the "Name" and "Page #" annotation fields at the top of the appropriate Continuation Page.

Don't forget to update the Index!

Additional Service/Repair Page for Equip/Appl
Named _____ on Page # _____

Service/Repair Date:	
Performed by:	
Service/Repair Accomplished:	
Service/Repair Date:	
Performed by:	
Service/Repair Accomplished:	
Service/Repair Date:	
Performed by:	
Service/Repair Accomplished:	
Service/Repair Date:	
Performed by:	
Service/Repair Accomplished:	
Service/Repair Date:	
Performed by:	
Service/Repair Accomplished:	

Continued on Page # _____

Additional Service/Repair Page for Equip/Appl Named _____ on Page # _____

Service/Repair Date:	
Performed by:	
Service/Repair Accomplished:	

Service/Repair Date:	
Performed by:	
Service/Repair Accomplished:	

Service/Repair Date:	
Performed by:	
Service/Repair Accomplished:	

Service/Repair Date:	
Performed by:	
Service/Repair Accomplished:	

Service/Repair Date:	
Performed by:	
Service/Repair Accomplished:	

Continued on Page # _____

Additional Service/Repair Page for Equip/Appl
Named _____ on Page # _____

Service/Repair Date:	
Performed by:	
Service/Repair Accomplished:	
Service/Repair Date:	
Performed by:	
Service/Repair Accomplished:	
Service/Repair Date:	
Performed by:	
Service/Repair Accomplished:	
Service/Repair Date:	
Performed by:	
Service/Repair Accomplished:	
Service/Repair Date:	
Performed by:	
Service/Repair Accomplished:	

Continued on Page # _____

Additional Service/Repair Page for Equip/Appl
Named _____ on Page # _____

Service/Repair Date:	
Performed by:	
Service/Repair Accomplished:	

Service/Repair Date:	
Performed by:	
Service/Repair Accomplished:	

Service/Repair Date:	
Performed by:	
Service/Repair Accomplished:	

Service/Repair Date:	
Performed by:	
Service/Repair Accomplished:	

Service/Repair Date:	
Performed by:	
Service/Repair Accomplished:	

Continued on Page # _____

Additional Service/Repair Page for Equip/Appl
Named _____ on Page # _____

Service/Repair Date:	
Performed by:	
Service/Repair Accomplished:	

Service/Repair Date:	
Performed by:	
Service/Repair Accomplished:	

Service/Repair Date:	
Performed by:	
Service/Repair Accomplished:	

Service/Repair Date:	
Performed by:	
Service/Repair Accomplished:	

Service/Repair Date:	
Performed by:	
Service/Repair Accomplished:	

Continued on Page # _____

Additional Service/Repair Page for Equip/Appl Named _____ on Page # _____

Service/Repair Date:	
Performed by:	
Service/Repair Accomplished:	
Service/Repair Date:	
Performed by:	
Service/Repair Accomplished:	
Service/Repair Date:	
Performed by:	
Service/Repair Accomplished:	
Service/Repair Date:	
Performed by:	
Service/Repair Accomplished:	
Service/Repair Date:	
Performed by:	
Service/Repair Accomplished:	

Continued on Page # _____

Additional Service/Repair Page for Equip/Appl
Named _____ on Page # _____

Service/Repair Date:	
Performed by:	
Service/Repair Accomplished:	

Service/Repair Date:	
Performed by:	
Service/Repair Accomplished:	

Service/Repair Date:	
Performed by:	
Service/Repair Accomplished:	

Service/Repair Date:	
Performed by:	
Service/Repair Accomplished:	

Service/Repair Date:	
Performed by:	
Service/Repair Accomplished:	

Continued on Page # _____

Additional Service/Repair Page for Equip/Appl Named _____ on Page # _____

Service/Repair Date:	
Performed by:	
Service/Repair Accomplished:	

Service/Repair Date:	
Performed by:	
Service/Repair Accomplished:	

Service/Repair Date:	
Performed by:	
Service/Repair Accomplished:	

Service/Repair Date:	
Performed by:	
Service/Repair Accomplished:	

Service/Repair Date:	
Performed by:	
Service/Repair Accomplished:	

Continued on Page # _____

Additional Service/Repair Page for Equip/Appl
Named _____ on Page # _____

Service/Repair Date:	
Performed by:	
Service/Repair Accomplished:	

Service/Repair Date:	
Performed by:	
Service/Repair Accomplished:	

Service/Repair Date:	
Performed by:	
Service/Repair Accomplished:	

Service/Repair Date:	
Performed by:	
Service/Repair Accomplished:	

Service/Repair Date:	
Performed by:	
Service/Repair Accomplished:	

Continued on Page # _____

Additional Service/Repair Page for Equip/Appl
Named _____ on Page # _____

Service/Repair Date:	
Performed by:	
Service/Repair Accomplished:	
Service/Repair Date:	
Performed by:	
Service/Repair Accomplished:	
Service/Repair Date:	
Performed by:	
Service/Repair Accomplished:	
Service/Repair Date:	
Performed by:	
Service/Repair Accomplished:	
Service/Repair Date:	
Performed by:	
Service/Repair Accomplished:	

Continued on Page # _____

Additional Service/Repair Page for Equip/Appl
Named _____ on Page # _____

Service/Repair Date:	
Performed by:	
Service/Repair Accomplished:	

Service/Repair Date:	
Performed by:	
Service/Repair Accomplished:	

Service/Repair Date:	
Performed by:	
Service/Repair Accomplished:	

Service/Repair Date:	
Performed by:	
Service/Repair Accomplished:	

Service/Repair Date:	
Performed by:	
Service/Repair Accomplished:	

Continued on Page # _____

Additional Service/Repair Page for Equip/Appl
Named _____ on Page # _____

Service/Repair Date:	
Performed by:	
Service/Repair Accomplished:	

Service/Repair Date:	
Performed by:	
Service/Repair Accomplished:	

Service/Repair Date:	
Performed by:	
Service/Repair Accomplished:	

Service/Repair Date:	
Performed by:	
Service/Repair Accomplished:	

Service/Repair Date:	
Performed by:	
Service/Repair Accomplished:	

Continued on Page # _____

Notes

INDEX

This Index is distinctly different. The basic Topics and their range of Page Numbers are already incorporated. However, the users are requested to identify the Names of the self-entered Equipment/Appliance Items and their associated Page Numbers. The same is true for the Continuation Pages.

Item Names and Page Numbers
to be Recorded by User

TOPIC/ITEM	PAGE #
Book Information	2 - 4
Introduction	5 - 20
Dealer/Seller and RV Information	21 - 31
Suggested List of Equip/Appl Items	32
Equipment/Appliance Information	33 - 74

Item Names and Page Numbers
to be Recorded by User

TOPIC/ITEM	PAGE #
Continuation of Service Record Info	75 - 88

Item Names and Page Numbers
to be Recorded by User

TOPIC/ITEM	PAGE #

All the Service Representatives,
Technicians, and Parts-Counter Workers
in the North American RV Industry
thank you for using this *Logbook*.

May you always be an
Informationally Wise,
Data Collection Attentive,
Posting Vigilant,
and
Responsible RV
Owner.

Sincerely,

Dale

Dale Lee Sumner

www.sumdalus.com

About the Author

Dale Lee Sumner is a retired RVIA/RVDA Master Certified RV Service Technician and former Owner/President of Mobile RV Medic, Inc.

He has over fifty-five years of experience using and living in RV's (including more than a decade of recent "full-timing"), conducting the business of repairing RVs, and, also, specializing in educating the RV owners.

And...Dale loves to teach what he writes! His goal is to provide as many RVers as possible – be they initially "Considering" RVing, just "Beginning" to RV, been "Camping" for years, or are "Full-Timers" – with a solid, baseline understanding of the different (non-house-like) functional areas in their RVs.

Dale's style is educational, yet casual and entertaining. He writes in a down-to-earth, non-technical fashion so every reader can easily become familiar with the subject(s).